A cat-shaped robot
born on September 3, 2112.
He rode a time machine all the way back from
the 22nd century to help Nobita.
He can pull all sorts of secret tools out of
the "4-D(Fourth Dimensional) Pocket"
on his tummy whenever Nobita needs them
to get himself out of trouble.

藤子・F・不二雄

Contents
もくじ

Slow and quick のろのろ、じたばた	7
The Nobita in the mirror かがみの中ののび太	23
"Hirari Manto" ひらりマント	31
Let's make badges バッジを作ろう	38
Black Belt Nobita 黒おびのび太	44
"Honmono Zukan" ほんもの図鑑（ずかん）	53
"Dokodemo Taihou" どこでも大ほう	64
"Ace cap" エースキャップ	70
Jekyll and Hyde ジキルハイド	75
Nobita's Bride のび太のおよめさん	84
To the beach by submarine せん水鑑で海へ行こう	94
"Hūko" the typhoon 台風のフー子	104
"Kobito Robot" 小人ロボット	113
Flying Fish 空とぶさかな	120
"Ultra Mixer" ウルトラミキサー	130
"Esper Boushi" エスパーぼうし	136
英語力を高めるワンポイントレッスン	153

Guide to the Book

この本の読み方

「うおう」の英訳。おどろきの声や効果音は、アメリカのまんが的な表現を使用したり、音のひびきを英語で表したりして、ふん囲気を出しています。英語辞書にのっていないものも、あります。

原作のまんがに合わせ、右開きですので、ふきだしは、右から左へと読んでください。

ROOOAR!

マントをふるんだ. 早く.

Hurry up and swing the cape.

Here he comes.

きた.

てんとう虫コミックス「ドラえもん」のまんがのセリフが、そのままついています。

おどろきの声や効果音は絵としてあつかっていますので、そのまま訳さずのせています。

まんがのセリフを英訳。特に意味を重視しながら訳しているので、原文には出てこない単語が英訳に出てくる場合があります。

「フエルミラー」.

"Fueru mirror."

ドラえもんのひみつ道具は、日本語部分では「」（かっこ）をつけています。

ドラえもんのひみつ道具は、英語部分では""（クオーテーションマーク）で表しています。原則として、ひみつ道具は斜体のローマ字で表していますが、外来語として定着している単語（クリーム、カメラ、ペンシルなど）は、英語で表示しました。

Slow and quick

のろのろ、じたばた

宿題なら，だめ．

I'll never help you with your homework!

<ruby>BUDDY<rt>きみ</rt></ruby>きみのだあいすきな
ドラやき……，

Here's your favorite dorayaki...

ドラえもんくん．

Dorae-mon.

てつだって
もらわないとまに
合わないんだもん．

But if you don't help, I can't finish it.

くりかえし
てるねえ．

day after day.

よくまあ，毎日毎日，
おんなじことを……，

Well, I wonder ... you only say the same thing

よくわかったな．

How did you know?

えっ？

Eh?

どう思う？

Well, what do you think?

このへんで，てっていてきに
反省してみる必要が，
あるんじゃないかな．

I think now might be a good time for you to really think things through.

どうして，
そうなるんだろうね．

Why do you always do this?

I guess you're right......

そういわれれば………．

なぜだろうかねえ．
……

I wonder ......

Well ......

モグ
モグ

**MUNCH
MUNCH**

そうねえ………．

8

はっきりいえば、のろまだ！ぐずだ！

To tell the truth, you're slow. You're a slacker.

のんびりしすぎてるんだよ。

You're too lax.

それがいけないんだよ.

That's the problem!.

こんや,ゆっくり考えてみる.

I'll think it over tonight.

のろまはうまれつきだい.

I'm just slow by nature.

ぱっぱっぱっぱっとね.

Quick! Quick!

やるべきことは,ぱっぱっとやらなくちゃ.

You should do what you have to do quickly.

HUFF

こっちが「クイック」. 気持ちも, からだの動きも,はやくなる. 「スロー」のほうは, そのぎゃく.

This is "QUICK". It'll speed up your feelings and actions. "SLOW" will do the opposite.

BAM!

薬はきらいなんだよ.

I hate medicine!

いいね. あとで…….

Sounds good. Later ......

きみは,「クイック」を飲みなさい.

Take some "QUICK".

9

ようし. ほんとにいい薬なら,ぼくも飲むよ.

All right.

Then if it's good medicine, I'll take it.

じゃ, まず自分で飲んでみせろ！

Fine, but you try it first!

SCRITCH SCRITCH SCRITCH

のび！

Nobi!

早く！ やれ！宿題！

Do your home-work!

Quickly!

のび太くんなんて,まどろっこしくって！ のびとはなんだ.

It takes too long to say 'Nobita-kun.'

What do you mean by Nobi!

ぱっぱとやんな. ぱっぱと.

Do it quickly. Quickly.

これからだよ. できたか？ できたか？

I'm just starting.

Are you finished? Are you finished?

おいっちに！　　　　**WAH-O!**

FIDGET　FRET
FIDGET　FRET

ぱっぱと　　　　　わからないところを，　　だめだよ，
行ってこい．　　　相談に行くんだ．　　　　さぼっちゃ．

人生は.　　のんびり　　せっかちは　　**Whew**　　ぱっぱ！
　　　　　行こうよ，　いやだなあ．

Rat-tat-tat　　じれったいな，もう.　　これから行くんだ.　　やあ，おかえり.

同時にとびこむ！

And rush in at the same time!

すばやく、よびりんをおす.

Ring the bell quickly.

なに、もたもたしてんの.

早く、早く.

Hurry up, hurry up.

Be quick about it!

POUND

タタダン

どな….

Who...

お茶ですか. ごちそうさまです.

Tea? Thank you very much.

あら、いらっしゃい.

Say hello while you take off your shoes.

Ah, wel-come.

やきいもは、食べるまえに おならをする.

Pass gas before you eat baked sweet potatoes.

飲む！早く！

Drink it! Quickly!

BOM

12

用事がまだなんだけど….

I haven't done what I came to do yet.

食べたら，さよなら．

When you finish, say good-bye.

あきれた！あきれた！

なにしてたんだ．

What a guy! What a guy!

What were you doing in there?

なに？

What?

SCREECH

たのむから「スロー」を飲んで，もとにもどってよ．

薬のききめはわかった．

やめてくれえ！

Please take "SLOW" and get back to normal.

I see how the medicine works now.

Stop it!

これだ，これだ，これだ．ゴクリ．

Here it is, here it is, here it is. GULP.

ええと，あれは，あれは….

よし，それじゃ！

Well, where was it, where was it...

All right!

飲む，飲む，飲む．

じゃ，きみ「クイック」を飲むか！飲むか！

OK, OK, OK.

Then you'll take "QUICK"? You'll take "QUICK"?

13

なに、やってんだ.
のろま！

早くおいつけえっ.

おうい、待てよ.

Hurry up.
You
slowpoke!

Faster!
Catch up!

Hey, wait.

ふう、ふう、
これじゃだめだ.

Puff-puff,
I can't do it.

こっちが「クイック」、こっちが「スロー」. まちがえるなんて、ばかだなあ.

あった.

ぼくも、
「クイック」を飲まなきゃ.

This one's "QUICK"
and this one's "SLOW".
What fool would take
the wrong one!

Here
it is.

I have to take
"QUICK",
too.

Droop!

こっちだ.

It was
this
one.

まちがえた……….

Wrong
one......

POP

ほっとけば,

Leave it

ウファー，ファー，
ファー，ファー.

Hwaah hwa
hwa

Haaaa-

フアー〜

ねえ. 消えるでしょ.

Right?

its
effect.

ききめが， いつか， 薬なら,

lose

eventu
-ally

The
med-
icine
will

いいや.

alone.

WHIZZ!

おうちへかえろ.

I'll go
home.

shuffle shuffle

WHIZZ!

ビュー

WHIZZ!

16

WHIZZ!

ジュ文

いまの風,
なにかしら.

What was
that wind?

まだみたい
だけど.

のび太くん
かえった？

のびのびのび
……．

トットット
……．

Not yet.

Is Nobita
home yet?

Nobi Nobi
Nobi.....

Ulppp
......

WHRR WHRR

バタバタ

くたびれた
よ，もう.

I'm so
tired.

CRASH!

ガチャ

こわれちゃう.

or I'll
snap.

早く，薬を
飲まないと,

I need to
take the
medicine
right
away,

気ばかり,
あせって.

からだは
くたくたなのに,

I can't
control my
impatience,

I'm dead
tired,
but...

はやいんだぞ. こう見えても, ぼくは, ものか. まける, なにを,

fast.

actually I'm

give up. never I'll

? がんばるぞ. でも,

? I'll do my best.

But,

I'm losing.

まけそうだなあ.

かたつむりさんと. きょうそう. なにやってんだ.

With a snail.

What are you doing?

A race.

きみ, きみ, きみ, きみ. まけたあ. きみははやいねえ.

Hey you, hey you, hey you, hey you.

You win. You're pretty fast.

知らないか, 知らないか.

Don't you know? Don't you know?

の, の, のび太.

No, No, Nobita.

な, な, なにを.

W, w, what?

教えろ, 教えろっ.

Tell me, tell me.

WHIZZ もういい. きかない！ じれったい.

ピュ〜〜

Fine. I won't ask you any more!

I can't wait.

早く教えろ. のび太なら ……….

Tell me quickly.

Nobita was ……

Quickly!

早く！

いまあ.

home.

ただ

I'm

だれか, あけてくれるのを 待ってたんだって.

He was just waiting for someone to open the door.

何をしてるんだ, そんなところで.

What are you doing there?

19 **Droop**

あ、 ひとつもらうよ.
Oh, I'll have one.

ほう，うまそうなドロップだ.
Wow, these candies look good.

それ，なんだ.
What are those?

POP じれったいな，早くいいなさい. それは…….

Hurry up and tell us.
Those are......

なんだい？ あのう.

What?
Uh...

RATTLE RATTLE RATTLE

TMP TMP

ておくれ…….

Too late......

TMP TMP

宿題やろう. ぼくもやっとなおった.

Let's do your homework.
At last I'm back to normal, too.

青森まで行ってきたよ. ヒーッ，やっと薬がきれた.

I went all the way to Aomori.
Phew, the medicine has finally worn off.

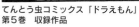
てんとう虫コミックス「ドラえもん」
第5巻　収録作品

The Nobita in the mirror

かがみの中ののび太

おやつは
ドラやきだよ.

Today's snack is dorayaki.

もっと，ちょ金しないと
買えないなあ.

I can't buy them if I don't save more money.

グラブにミニカーに
うでどけい…….

A glove, a minicar and a wrist watch......

ラジコン戦車が5680円だろ.
トランシーバーが6500円だろ.

A radio-controlled tank costs 5680 yen.
A transceiver costs 6500 yen.

100円よ.

It's 100 yen.

これ，いくら?

How much is this?

これみんな，
友だちが
持ってんだよ.

But my friends have all of these.

やたらに，ものを
ほしがるんじゃ
ないよ.

You shouldn't be so greedy.

まだまだ，買えないなあ.

I still need more.

返すから，その分
お金でちょうだい.

I'll give it back, so give me the money.

うまそうだねえ.

That looks good.

じゃあ，
すきなようにしろ.

All right, suit yourself.

どうせきみは,
そういうやつなんだ.

That's the kind of guy you are, after all.

わかってます. 半分
もらおうなんて
思わないよ.

I know. I'm not thinking you'll share.

あのね, これは
ぼくの分だから….

Look, this one's mine.

SWITCH

「フエルミラー」.

"*Fueru* mirror."

食べられや
しない.

How am I supposed to eat?

うつしたものが, ほんものに
なって出てくるんだ.

Anything reflected in the mirror comes out as the real thing.

R-R-RRR

なに
やってんの？

What are you doing?

R-R-RRR

なんでも
買えるぞ.

We can buy anything.

そうだ, お金をふやそう.

I have an idea. Let's multiply money.

すごいかがみだ.

What a mirror!

スイッチを切りわすれたら
たいへん.

If you forget to turn off the switch, there will be trouble.

そうだ．なにも，お金を出して買わなくてもいいんだ．

I've got it. We don't need to get more money.

かがみだから，あべこべのが出てくる．

This is a mirror, so you'll get money printed in reverse.

どうして？

Why not?

だめ．

It's no good.

ふやしてかえせばいいんだ．

I only have to multiply and then return them.

ほんとに，30分でいいんだな．

Are you sure it's just for 30 minutes?

きっとかえせよ．

Be sure to return this to me.

かりちん10円ずつはらうから．

I'll pay you 10 yen as a rental fee.

R-R-RRR CLICK

おわったあ．

I'm done.

スイッチ切っとけよ．

Don't forget to turn off the switch.

RUSTLE
RUSTLE

うつしてはとり出し，うつしてはとり出し．

Reflect and take out. Reflect and take out.

26

R-R-RRR

ルルル

R-R-RRR

ゆめみたいだ. こんなに
いっぺんに, ぼくのものに
なるなんて.

It's like a dream to
have them all at
once.

ぼく, のび太.

I'm
Nobita.

だ, だれだ?

W, who
are you?

WAH!

ワッ

SHOOP

そっちがかがみへ
はいれ.

YOU go into
the mirror.

PLOP

もどれ.

Go
back!

かがみから
出たな.

You came out
of the mirror,
didn't
you?

出られないよう.

I can't
get out.

わあ, まっくらだあ.

Ah! It's
pitch-
dark.

CLICK

パチ

THUMP

ドスン

27

用がすんだら，
かたづけなよ．

なんだなんだ． ドラえもん．

まだ遊んでるの．

いっぺん，かがみの外へ，
出たかったんだ．さあ，うんと遊ぼう．

えんぴつ，いつから左手で持つように
なったの．ちゃんとやりなさい．

けさから，あとであとでって，
ちっとも勉強しないじゃないの．

いま，遊びはじめた
とこだよ．

ふやして食べれば
いいや．

そうだ！
ちょっとかりて，

ドラやき，もうひとつ
食べたい．

GASP

R-R-RRR

CLICK

にせもの！

an imposter!

え，じゃあ，
さっきのは．

What? Then, he was...

のび太だよう．

I'm Nobita.

ぼく，こんなへんな
顔してたかな．

Do I really look this weird?

ぼく，帰る．こんなきびしい
世界はこりごりだい．

I'm going back. I've had enough of this strict world.

"Hirari Manto"

ひらりマント

ぶんなぐってやるぞ.

Wait!

まてぇ

I'm going to beat you up.

ジャイアンにあわないように,
ずうっとうちにいよう.

I'll just stay home so I won't see Gian.

おぼえてろっ. こんどあったら,
ただじゃおかないからな.

Just remember. Next time I see you, you're going to get it.

どうせ遊んでるんなら,
お使いぐらいしてくれたっていいでしょ.

If you're just fooling around, you might as well run this errand.

いやだ, いやだ.

のびちゃん,
お手紙出してきて.

No, no.

Nobi-chan, mail this letter for me.

これを持っていくと、
いいや.

Just carry this
with you.

こまった.

I'm in
trouble.

ぼくにむかって
とびかかってみな.

Come charging
at me.

なんだい,
そのふろしきみたいなもの.

What's that? It looks
like a wrapping cloth.

こうかい.

Like this?

BANG

DASH

33

CRASH

やったなあ.

Darn you!

これがあれば，なにがきても
こわくないや.

気をつけて歩きなさい.

あっ，先生.

> I'm not afraid of anything as long as I have this.

> Watch where you're going.

> Oh, sir.

BOWWOW

35

雨がよけていくよ.

The rain isn't falling on us.

雨だ.

It's raining.

かわかしておこう.

Let's dry it in the sun.

マントはぐっしょり.

The cape is soaking wet.

もう，やんだ.

It stopped.

ただいま.

I'm home.

FLAP

ふわり

36

CRASH

FLAP FLAP

CRASH

へんだな.

That's strange.

FLAP FLAP

どうしても,
うちにはいれないよう.

No matter what I
do, I can't get into
the house.

Let's make badges

バッジを作ろう

よく集めたなあ.

これ, みんな,
スネ夫くんのバッジ?

What a collection!

Are these all your badges, Suneo?

でも, 3ばんね.

わたし, たった6こ.

おれ, 18こだから, ぼくが, なんたって
2ばんね. 1ばんだね. 63こ
あるんだ.

But I'm No.3.

I only have 6.

I have 18, so I'm No.2.

I'm absolutely No.1.

I have 63 badges.

JINGLE

3人できょうそう わたしも, もっと ようし, がんばって
しよう. 集めるわ. 1ばんになるぞ. ぼく, 1こで4ばん.

Let's compete among three of us.

I'll collect more, too.

OK. I'll collect more and become No.1.

I have 1, so I'm No.4.

バッジがほしいよう.

I want badges!

ぼくがほしいのは，
バッジだよ.

Hey, it's badges that I want.

持ってるの.

Do you have some?

KLICK!

BEEP

写すと，バッジになる
カメラだよ.

This camera will make a badge out of anything you photograph.

ほんものみたいだ.

VROOM...   **CLICK!**

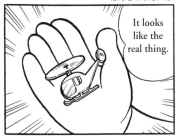

It looks like the real thing.

40

まず，かいじゅうの
バッジを作ろう．

ありがとう．
ドラえもん．

それで，百でも，二百でも，
作ればいい．

First, let's make
monster badges.

Thank you.
Doraemon.

Using this camera,
you can make
hundreds of badges.

うわっ
どんどんできちゃうよ．

PLUNK

**CLICK
CLICK**

Wow, they
just keep
coming out!

PLUNK

まんがの
バッジも作ろう．

**CLICK
CLICK**

いいね．

こん虫や動物のも
作ろうよ．

And some
comic
book
badges.

All
right.

Let's make
insect and
animal badges,
too.

WAH!

これ，みんな，
バッジ？

**CLANKETY-
CLANK**

どうだっ．

Are these
all badges?

What do
you think
of this?

41

ようし．ドラえもんバッジと，のび太バッジを作ってみせよう． うそだ．そんなことできるもんか． そのカメラで作ったって？

ひとりでに写してくれるんだね． 自動シャッターで，

CLICK CLICK

おれも．着がえて，くるわ．ほんと． きみたちのバッジも，作ってあげよう．

あれっ． **SQUEAK** おまちどお．

てんとう虫コミックス「ドラえもん」第5巻　収録作品

Black Belt Nobita

黒おびのび太

へえっ, すげえな.

おれな, とうちゃんにじゅう道ならってるんだぞ.

Sounds great.

I'm taking judo lessons from my dad.

教えて, 教えて.

おまえたちにも, 教えてやろうか.

Teach us, teach us.

Shall I teach you?

44

かあっこいい！ **DAHHHHH!**

はっ.

GASP.

Cool!

First, you grab him like this.

Some other time...

まず,
こうやってだな.

ま, また,
こんどにしようね.

YANK

男なら投げかえせ！

そんなめにあわされて，だまって帰ってきたのか！

Be a man! Throw him down!

And you just came home with your tail between your legs?

…というわけ.

... and that's what happened.

ぎゃっ，くちゅぐったい！

何か，強くなるものをかしてよ.

Stop it! That tickles!

Can you lend me anything that will make me become strong?

だって，こわいんだもの.

But I'm scared.

どんな相手でも，きみにさわったやつは，みんな，投げとばされるんだ.

こんなのしめるだけで，強くなるの.

Whoever touches you will be flung away.

Can I really become strong just by wearing this?

？

じゃ，これでも使ってみるか.

？

Well then, let's try this.

A "black belt" that makes you good at judo.

じゅう道に強くなる「ブラックベルト」…．

わっ，さわるな．
Oh, don't touch me.

ドラえもん，ありがとう！
Doraemon, thank you!

そうとも！
That's right!

これで，ジャイアンのやつにしかえしができる．
Using this, I can get even with Gian.

Anyone you touch will be flung away automatically.

さわると，自動てきに投げちゃうんだから．

めざすは，ジャイアンただひとり．
I'm only after Gian.

気をつける．
I'll be careful.

めざす相手のほか，さわるんじゃないぜ．
Don't touch anybody you're not aiming for.

おい，もう一度じゅう道やろう．
Hey, let's try judo again.

いたっ．
There he is.

弱すぎて，あほらしくて
相手にならんよ.

You're too weak.
You're no match
for me.

さあ，どこからでも
かかってこい！

OK,
come on!

なにやってんだ，
こいつ.

What is he
doing?

WHAM　　**SLIP**

こっちから
行くぞっ.

I'll
attack
you.

ようし！

Fine!

あら，のび太さん，
どうしたの.

Hey, Nobita,
what happened?

まてえっ，あいたた……
ちくしょう！

Wait, oh, ow......
Darn you!

ほおら，
やっちゃった.

See? I told
you.

どろをはらって
あげるのよ.

I'm just
going to
brush the
dirt off
your
clothes.

わっ，さわらないで！

No, don't
touch me!

あっ，先生，ぼくに
さわるとあぶないよ.

こら，女の子を
投げとばすとは，
なにごとです.

なんとおわびして
よいやら.

No, don't touch me. I'm warning you.

How can I ever apologize?

What do you think you're doing throwing a girl?

See? I told you.

You're threatening me?

だから，いったのに.

先生をおどかす
気か.

さわらないでえ！

Don't touch me!

OH! Please forgive us.

こんなおび，
はずしちゃえ.

I'll just take it off.

ふうふう，はあはあ.

Pant-pant, puff-puff.

わあい, これなら, えんりょなく投げられる.

Yahoo, now, I can fling them away with no problem.

なかったら, 家へとりに行け.

If you don't have any, go home and get some.

やい, こづかいよこせ.

Come on, give us your money.

このやろう.

You dirty......

いらっしゃい. いいから, いいから.

けがをしたく なかったら, ひっこんでいろ.

なんだ, おまえは.

Come on.

Whatever. Whatever.

If you don't want to get hurt, keep out of it!

Who are you?

DAHHHHHH!

ここにあったわ.
Oh, here it is.

おびをどこへしまったかしら.
Where did I put that belt?

なんだ, いないのか.
Hmm, he isn't here.

ドラえもん,「ブラックベルト」をかえすよ.
Doraemon, I'll give the "black belt" back now.

Oh, no!

やったあ!

ほどけるまで, よりつかないほうがいいよ.
We have to keep away from him till he gets it off.

なに, そんなぶっそうなおびか?
What? The belt's that dangerous?

But I can't, because she tied it funny.

I'll untie it at once.

すぐ, ほどこう.

へんなむすび方したからほどけない.

Anyone you touch
will be flung away
automatically.

"Honmono Zukan"

ほんもの図鑑

あはははは. ほんとかい. それが, のび太に そっくりなんだ. メガネザルって 遠い南の国に. のがいるんだ.

A ha ha ha. Really? They look just like Nobita.

And they live far to the south. There are things called "tarsiers."

そんなこといわれて, なぜおこらない. メガネザルそっくり だって. はりあいないや. あれ, 悪口いわれても おこらないの.

Why didn't you get angry about that? He said you looked like tarsiers?

Then what's the point of teasing him? Hey, he doesn't even care if you insult him.

どんなすてきなサルか, 図鑑で調べよう. ぼくに似てるなら, よっぽどりっぱな顔のサルだろ.

I'll look up them in the picture book to see how wonderful they are.

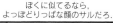

If they look like me, they must be pretty good-looking monkeys. Why should I?

どうしておこるの.

そんな大事な本は, かしちゃだめなんだよ. 友だちにかした時, やぶかれたんだ. 悪いやつだな. あれっ, サルのページがない!

You shouldn't lend such an important book.

When I lent it to my friend, he must have torn the pages out. What a jerk!

Hey! The pages on monkeys are missing!

もういい.
しまってくれ.

なるほど似てる.

ほんものをみられるのが,
この図鑑の特ちょうだよ.

That's enough. Put him back.

He really does look like you.

You can see the real thing. That's the advantage of this picture book.

CHATTER

これでよし.

もどれ.

CHATTER

There we go.

Get back in.

大事に使うから.
ねえ, かしてよ.

だめっ. ほんものだから,
なくなるとこまるんだ.

いい図鑑だね.
かしてよ.

I'll be carefull. Come on, lend them to me.

No. They are the real things, so I'll be in big trouble if you lose them.

What great picture books! Lend them to me.

火事
だ.

Fire!

There's smoke coming out of Nobita's room.

のび太のへやから,
けむりがでてる.

PUFF PUFF

56

ちがうよ. 入道雲は,
夏にでるんだぞ. かみなりがなって, けむりじゃないぞ.
夕立がふるんだ. 入道雲だ.

No. We can only see those in the summer. They bring thunder and showers.

That's not smoke. It's a thunderhead!

RUMBLE
ZAAAAA RUMBLE FLASH

「ほんもの図鑑」だって！

ほかにも,
いろいろあるよ.

この図鑑で
だしたんだ.

"Honmono Zukan"?

I have a lot of others.

I let it out of this picture book.

おてんき

57

おれにも. ぼくにも. かしてくれ.

Me, too.

Me, too.

Lend one to me.

とりかえしてくるから.

I'll get them back.

きみの友だちは, かりた本を
やぶるようなやつだろ.

Aren't they the kind of guys who tear pages out of the books they borrow?

えっ, もっていかれたって.

What! Your friends took the books home?

やったな.

Oh, no!

だめっ, すぐかえせ.

No, give it back right now.

ちょっとくらい,
いいじゃんか.

Just a little longer.

かってかえすよ.

I'll buy you new ones.

おかしを食べちゃった.

He ate all the snacks.

デコレーションケーキ　チョコレー

ショートケーキ　クリー

ホットケーキ

せっかくめずらしいのが，
手にはいったと思ったのに．

And here I thought I'd finally found some rare ones.

ちょうがたりない．

Some butterflies are missing!

ひと回りしてからかえすよ．

HONK HONK

ひょっとしたら，それ
「乗り物図鑑」の車じゃないか．

We'll give it back after we take a spin.

Isn't that a car from "the picture book of vehicles"?

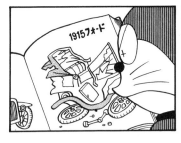

CRASH

だれかきてえ！

Someone, save me!

59

まだ，1冊たりない．

No, one of them is still missing.

みんなもどってよかったね．

We got them all back. What a relief.

YEOW!

きっと，スネ夫だ．

「大むかしの生きもの」
という図鑑だ．

I'm sure Suneo will have it.

It's "the picture book of ancient creatures".

どうして，マンモスなんか
だしたんだい．

Why did you let a mammoth out of the book?

60

SNORT SNORT!

おこらせたら，手の
つけようがないんだ．

If we make him angry, there's nothing we can do.

さわいじゃだめっ.

Be quiet!

ぞうさん，
おはなが長い……

Mr. elephant, you have such a long trunk.

静かな歌で，
気を静めさせよう.

Let's calm him down with a soft song.

ぞうさん大好きよう.

I love you, Mr. elephant.

すてきなぞうさん，
いいぞうさん.

Nice Mr. elephant, lovely Mr. elephant.

しめた.
うっとりときいてるぞ.

It worked! He's charmed!

GLARE

TIP TOE

BHUAUGH!

BAM

Oh, the book!

あっ，図鑑が.

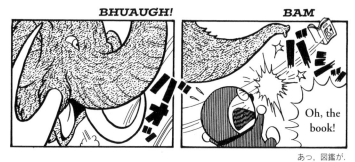

にげろ.

Run away!

TAP TAP

「お話図鑑」で，
強い人間をだそう.

I'll let strong people out of "the picture book of stories".

だめだ.

They're useless.

WAAAH   **STOMP STOMP**

FLUMP   **ZOOOM**

I did it.

うまくいった.

だしてくれえ.

のび太くん，マンモスは図鑑に
もどったから，もう安心だよ.

Let me out!

のび太

マンモス

マストド

Nobita-kun, the mammoth is back in the book, so you can relax now.

I'm in here.

てんとう虫コミックス「ドラえもん」
第6巻　収録作品

ここだよう.

"Dokodemo

どこでも大ほう

おとうさんののる列車は
どこにいるかな.

？

？

Where's
the train you want
to take?

この中へ入って.

Get inside.

BANG

はっしゃ.

これだ.

Go!

That's it.

ZOOM

WHIZZZ

のれてよかったね.

He made it!

みんな集まってるぞ. テレビにうつればね. どこでもいけるの？

Everybody's getting together.

Yeah, if you can see it on the TV.

I can go any-where?

よしきた. あそこへおくって.

All right.

Send me there.

きゃっ, かみなり. **THUD**

Eek, thunder!

RUMBLE RUMBLE

ほら, あれだよ. えっ, 大ほうでとんで きたって.

See! That's it.

What? You flew here by a cannon?

パパの会社へ，
おべんとうをとどけて．

Send this lunch to my dad's company.

おねがいするわ．

Thanks.

さあ，どこへでも，
運んであげるよ．

We can send you anywhere.

外国へいきてえ．

I wanna leave the country.

お花見にいきたい．

We want to go see the cherry blossoms.

ゴミをだしてきて．

Send the garbage out.

こづつみを，いなかへ
とどけて．

Send this package to my hometown.

おれは，銀行ギャングだ．
これから，外国へにげるんだ．

I'm a bank robber and I'm leaving the country.

Shut up!

うるせえ．

じゅんばんを守ってよ．

Wait your turn.

あんただれ．

Who are you?

うひい．

Ohhhh.

さっさとしないと
うつぞっ．

Be quick, or I'll shoot you!

じゃ，外国へいく
船にのせろ．

Then, send me to an outbound ship.

こ，この大ほうは，
外国までとどかないよ．

TH, the cannon won't reach as far as another country.

あれがいい, のせろ.

There! Put me on that ship.

あれれ, まだ港につかないのに.

これでおれさまは安全ににげられる.

What? I haven't reached the port yet.

Now I can get away safely.

作ったばかりの, 船のプラモデルの上に落ちたんだって.

He fell onto a newly made model ship.

CRASH

てんとう虫コミックス「ドラえもん」
第6巻 収録作品

69

"Ace cap"

エースキャップ

つまり，ねらった所に
あたればいいんだろ.

So, you just want to hit
what you're aiming at,
right?

まあ，そうがっかりすんな.

Don't be so
upset.

どんなに練習してもだめだ.
ぼくは，才能がないんだな.

No matter how
hard I practice, I
can't do it. I have
no talent for
throwing.

名投手になれる！

And you
can be an
excellent
pitcher!

かぶるだけでいいんだ.

Just wear
this.

「エースキャップ」

"Ace cap."

こっちをむいてなげても
まとにあたる.

you'll hit it even
if you throw
looking this way.

たとえば，きみがあのまとに
あてようと思えば，

For example, if you
think about hitting
that target,

FWOOO

SPIN

ははは，まさか.

Ha, ha, ha,
No way!

スウ

クルッ

あれ，あれ，あれ.

Wha...
Wha...
Wha...!

71

それで，だい活やく
　　できるよ.　こりゃおどろいた！　**BAMM**

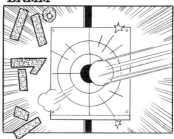

たとえば，こうやって
ねそべっていて……….　えっ？野球なんかしない？
じゃ，なんのための練習？　さあ，はりきっていこう！
相手チームをばったばったと
三しんにしちゃおう！

くずかごまで，はるばるすてに
いくのも，めんどくさい.　この紙を，そのへんに
ほうりだしておくわけには
いかないし…,　はなをかんだとする.

HONK

PLOP　そこで，えいっと….

72

きちんともどしておける.
読みおわった本も……,

It goes right back in the bookcase.

And the book I'm finished with......

ろくなことないぞ.
子どものくせに，そんなにめんどくさがってると,

If you're that lazy when you're just a kid,

you'll have problems later.

あきれた！　ほんとにもう…,

believe it!

I can't even

ストライク.

Strike!

のび太，さっきたばこかってきてもらった時のおつりは？

Nobita, give me the change for the cigarettes you bought for me.

STRETCH

ぼくの悪口いってるな.

They're insulting me.

ほんと！
あのばかが.

このあいださ，
のび太のばかが…….

Really! That fool.

The other day, that fool Nobita...

Nobita, it's Shizu-chan......

Where did it come from?

It's chewed gum.

ベトー

GLOP

To wherever Shizu-chan is.

What if I throw myself?

Wait ...

まてよ….

What a hassle!

Shizu-chan is calling him all the way from Hokkaido...

Where did he go?

?

ZOOM

?

Jekyll and Hyde

ジキルハイド

GLARE いいどきょうだなあ. そ, そういうんだ.

つまり, おまえにかりた望遠鏡を,
今すぐ返せと………,
こういうんだな.

You've got a lot of guts.

ギロッ

So you're saying, I should give back the telescope I borrowed from you...... Right?

R, right.

I see ......

ほう……,

You can't stare me down. I'm not leaving.

に, にらんでも帰らないぞ！

さあ, なぐるならなぐれ.

いつもその手で, かした物
とられちゃうんだ. きょうこそ,
返してくれるまで帰らない！

If you're going to hit me, go ahead and do it.

You always use that trick to keep my stuff, but not this time. I won't go home until you give it back!

つい友だちにかりて……,
つかってるうちに, 自分の
みたいな気がしてきて…….

おれ……, ほしいものなんでも
かってもらえないんだ.

わかったよ.
わるかったよ.

So I borrow something from a friend..., and while I'm using it, I start feeling like it's mine......

My......, my dad won't buy me the things I want.

It's alright. I'm in the wrong.

76

もう，しばらくかしとく．

You can keep it for a while.

おれがまちがってた．
さあ早くもって帰ってくれ！

I was wrong. You can take it back.

どうだ．ぼくの教えたとおりに
したら，返してくれたろ．

How was it? If you did as I told you, he gave it back. Right?

へへへ，あいつ，
おひとよしだなあ． ばあか！

Heh, heh, heh. He's an easy mark. Fool!

あきれた！

I don't believe it.

かわいそうになって． えっ，おいてきた？

I felt sorry for him.

What! You left it at his house?

ドラえもんにまでみはなされちゃ，
ぼくは………，どうしたらいいんだ．

If even you give up on me......, what can I do?

つきあいきれない，もう． ほんとにもう！

I won't help you anymore!

I've had enough.

You're too kind-hearted or maybe you're just coward.

おひとよしというか，
気が弱いというか．

かして，かして．

Lend it to me, lend it to me.

ちょっとのあいだなら，くすりでなおせるよ．

If it's only for a short time, there's a medicine.

この気の弱いの，なんとかなおせないかなあ．

I want to get rid of this cowardliness somehow.

望遠鏡をとりかえしたら，返すから．

If I get back the telescope from him, I'll return it to you.

あまりいいくすりじゃないんだよ．

I can't recommend this medicine.

やはりやめよう．

No, I better not.

これをのむと，ひとつぶにつき10分間，まるっきりひとがらがあべこべになる，おそろしいくすりだ．

If you take this pill, your personality will become its exact opposite for 10 minutes. It's a horrible medicine.

「ジキルハイド」というくすり．

It's called "Jekyll and Hyde".

Grrr

HICCUP

たった10分間．

For only 10 minutes.

ジャイアン.

10分しかないんだ.
てっとりばやく
やらなきゃ.

Gian!

The medicine only works for 10 minutes. I have to do it quickly.

望遠鏡をとり返したら,
くすりを返すんだよ.

When you get the telescope back, give me back the medicine.

OK.

わかってる.

ウーーウーー………

Grrr...,
grrr......

いまトイレだ.
おわるまでまってろ.

I'm in the bathroom. Wait until I'm finished.

POP おう,なんだ.

Yeah, what?

おそいよ.

おう,
用ならあがれ.

You're too late.

Okay, come in.

早くしてくれない
かなあ.ウーー.

こまるなあ,10分
たったら
きれちゃうのに.

Hurry up!
Grrr...

Oh, no! It'll wear off in 10 minutes.

DROOP

GIAN!

!

POP

望遠鏡のことじゃないだろうな.
あれなら,話はすんでるからな.

You're not here about the telescope, are you. We already settled that.

80

なんだとはなんだ.

おれにむかって
その口のききかたはなんだ.

Who are you to talk?

How dare you talk to
me like that!

DROOP

また，きれたあ.

It wore
off again.

ショボ

早く,
時間がない.

おっかねえの．返すよ．ええと,
どこにしまったかな.

Hurry up,
there's no
time.

How intimidating. I'll give it
back to you. Let's see...,
where is it?

なんだこりゃ？

What's this?

ふたがとれ
なくなった.

よくもおどかし
やがって，このう.

きゅうに,
こわくなくなったぞ.

I can't
get the
lid off.

How
dare you
threaten
me!

Suddenly,
you're
not so
scary.

**GOBBLE
GOBBLE**

強くなるくすりを
のんでたのか！

You took
medicine to
make you
stronger.

コポ

ははあ，さっきから
へんだへんだと思ったら,

返してよ.

Now I see why
you've been acting
strangely.

Give it
back.

POP

81

ドラえもおん！

全部のんだ！

ウーフー
…….

ヒクッ,

Doraemon!

He took all of them!

Ummm, Hooo.....

Hiccup,

おっそろしいことになるぞ.

ただでさえ,
らんぼうなやつが.

ひとびん全部？

He'll be terrible!

He's violent as it is, so...

The whole bottle?

あの……, のび太さん
いらっしゃるかしら.

夜にげしよう.

なにをされるか
わからない.

Excuse me......, is Nobita-san in?

Let's sneak out at night.

Who knows what he'll do.

？

望遠鏡やなんか, いままで
おかりしたものです.

おそかった！

?

I brought the telescope and everything else I've ever borrowed.

We're too late!

乱ほうなひとがらが変わって，
おとなしくなったんだ．

His violent personality
changed into a gentle one.

あたしって，いけない子だったわ．
ゆるしてちょうだいね．

I've been so bad.
Please forgive me.

SOB SOB

てんとう虫コミックス「ドラえもん」
第6巻　収録作品

Bride

およめさん

This little baby

このあかんぼが、

has gotten so big.

もうこんなに大きくなっちゃって。

Time flies. It feels like you just entered kindergarten, but...

早いものねえ。ついこの間ようち園にはいったと思ってたら。

Here you are in elementary school.

もう、りっぱな小学生。

Happy birthday!

お誕生日おめでとう。

Nobita's

のび太の

あとわずかで中学か……

> Soon you'll be in junior high school......

そしたらすぐ高校……大学……

> And then high school......, and college......

だまれ！

> Shut up!

はいれればだけど.

> If they let you in.

大学を卒業したら、いちにんまえのおとなだからな.

> After graduating from college, you'll be all grown-up.

その次はおよめさんね.

> And after that, you'll get married.

うるさいぞ, もう!

> Shut up, already!

> If someone is willing to marry you.

だれかきてくれればだけど.

85

しかし…….

But......

まてっ, やいこら!

Come here, you!

やあい, てれちゃってる.

Oh, you're blushing!

おい, 本気でそんな
心配してるの?

Are you really worried about that?

もしも, ぼくにだけ
およめさんのきてが
なかったら, どうしよう.

What if I'm the only one who can't get married?

なにが?

About what?

心配になってきたぞ.

You got me worried.

えっ, 「タイム・マシン」で
ぼくのおよめさんを?

What! Use your "Time Machine" to go see my future bride?

みにいくって……,
なにを?

Go and see......, what?

そんなに気になるなら,
みにいってきたら?

If you're so worried, why not go and see?

どっちだよ.

Make up your mind.

ぜひみたあい.

But I'm dying to see her.

じゃ,
やめとけ.

Then, don't.

そ, そんな……, とても
ぼくは……, はずかしい.

Oh, no......, I'm too......, shy.

86

ついたぞ.

Here we are.

そのころならいくらきみでも、だれかあいてがみつかってるよ.

Even you can find someone to marry by that time.

Let's go forward 25 years from now.

25年後へいこう.

あれえ？

What the...

トイレの中にでちゃった.

We came out in the bathroom.

トイレばっかり.

There's nothing but bathrooms!

町のようすがすっかりかわってる.

The town has changed completely.

ぼくの家が、公しゅう便所になってる.

My house has become a public toilet.

10年前に.

あのマンションに
ひっこしたよ.

ああ，あそこにたってた
野比さんの家ね.

10 years ago.

They moved to that apartment.

Oh, the Nobi family who used to live there?

12階の68号室
だって.

このへんは公園に
なっちゃったんだ.

He said Room 68 on the 12th floor.

This area's a park now.

ちょ，ちょっとまって！

ここだ.

W, wait a minute!

Here.

88

? 悪い子ね. さあつかまえた.

なにわかりきったこと いってるの，ママにむかって. 25年前の源静香さん！ ひょっとしてあんたは…….

さあ，わかんない. とにかくいってらっしゃい. これ どういうこと？ よくおわびしなさい！ さあ，はいりなさい．スネ太郎くんのママがかんかんよ.

ははあ……. ようく，しかってください よ. ほんとにうちのノビスケはわんぱくで. いつもいつも，よくもうちのスネ太郎をなかしてくれるわね.

ばんざい！

H-U-R-

R-A-Y!

そのママがしずかちゃんだ．
ということは，
つまり…つまり……．

And his mom is
Shizuka-chan.
That means...
that means......

ノビスケってのは，ぼくと
そっくりの顔で……，
つまりぼくのむすこだ！

If Nobisuke looks
like me......, he must
be my son!

ママにむかって
きみとはなんです．

What do you
mean saying
"YOU" like that
to your mother?

そうか
きみだったのか．　しあわせえ！

So, it's
you, is it?

I'm so
happy!

わあ，なにするんだよ！

パパはあんなにのんびりした，おとなしい人
なのに，おまえはどうしてきかんぼなの？

やめてえ，人ちがいだあ！

WAH,
what are you
doing!

Stop it,
I'm not who
you think I am.

Your dad is so
quiet and gentle,
why are you so
naughty?

SPANK SPANK

わかった？
？　あれがノビスケ！

？

See? That's
Nobisuke!

あっ！

ただいま．

I'm home.

Eh!

91

Nobisuke!
Stop being so naughty.
Have you been studying?

Who are you!
What are you
doing here!

Oh, my
good-
ness......

Mom, he's an alien.
He must be planning to
impersonate me and
conquer this house!

How dare
you hit
your own
father!

BONK!

Get into
the "Time
Machine"
quickly!

Run away,
Doraemon!

There
you are.

Hurry up!

Oh, no. It's
occupied.

Ahem,
ahem.

BANG-BANG

元気で
いいじゃない.

なんて
らんぼうな子だ.

You should be happy he's so energetic.

What a violent kid!

しずかちゃんがお祝いに
きてくださったのよ.

どこへ
いってたの.

Shizuka-chan is here to celebrate your birthday.

Where have you been?

!

おかしな子ね!

どうしてそんなに
はずかしがるのよ.

What a strange boy!

Why are you so shy?

てんとう虫コミックス「ドラえもん」第6巻　収録作品

94

To the beach by submarine

せん水艦で海へ行こう

Hurry up!

I'll go ask my mom for permission.

いそいでね.

おかあさんにことわってくるわ.

Of course. I'm your friend. Now wait a minute. I'll take out the submarine.

Whenever something bad happens, you help me. You're so good to me.

あったりまえだ. 友だちだもん. まってろ, せん水かんをだすから.

ぼくがいやなめにあうと, いつも, たすけてくれる. きみは, いいやつだなあ.

Who needs a motor-boat! Don't ride in it.

モーターボート がなんだ. のるな のるな.

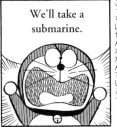

We'll take a submarine.

こっちはせん水かんでいこう.

The "Sub-marine".

What's that?

「せん水かん」. なにそれ.

This is it.

これだ.

BLOOP

I wasn't trying to fool you.

べつに, からかって なんかいないよ.

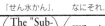

水にいれると，まわりの広さにあわせて
のびちぢみするんだ．

BLOOP BLOOP

If you put it in water, it expands or contracts to fit the surroundings.

わかってるよ．
海へいくよ．

ふろばでせん水かんに
のったって，ちっとも
おもしろくない．

さあ，のりなよ．

I know. We're going to the beach.

It's no fun riding in a submarine in the bathroom.

Now, get on board.

くりかえせば，どこへでも
いける．水なんか
どこにでもあるから．

あんまり遠くの水へは，
とどかないけどね．

これは，水から水へ，
ジャンプできるんだ．

If we keep jumping, we can go anywhere. Because we can find water everywhere.

But it can't jump too far.

This submarine can jump from water to water.

JUMP JUMP

CLICK

では，
さいしょのジャンプ．

海なら，ここから南へ
すすめばいいんだ．

Here's the first jump.

We can go to the beach if we go south from here.

まさか．

こおりがういてる．
南極だ．

こ，
ここは．

FOOM

Icebergs! We're at the South Pole!

No way!

Where are we?

POOF

98

SLURP

RATTLE RATTLE

FOOM

わあっ, ジャンプ.

WAH, jump!

RATTLE RATTLE

おばけざかな.

A giant fish!

つぎへジャンプ.

金ぎょばちだよ.

We're in a goldfish bowl.

Let's take the next jump!

99

ジャンプ ジャンプ.

Jump, jump!

WAAAH!

キャア

?

GLUB GLUB
GLUB

ゴボ
ゴボ ゴボ

みどり色に,
どろっと
にごってる.

The water
is all green
and
cloudy.

どこだい,
ここは.

Where
are we?

ジャンプ.

BLECCH CRUNCH

Jump!

ガリ

ぎゅう. ジャンプ.

Squish. Jump!

もうすぐ海だ.

へんなとこ ばっかり.

ジャンプ ジャンプ.

We'll get to the beach soon.

We keep ending up in weird places.

Jump, jump!

こんどのジャンプで, まちがいなく海につくぞ.

The next jump should take us to the beach.

Are you sure?

きっとか.

まちがいない.

ここが海.

This is the ocean?

Absolutely.

やけどしちゃう.
たすけてえ.

Ow, ow!

We'll get burned. HELP US!

Why is it so hot?

なんだか, ばかにあついよ,

VROOOM

同じことばかりいってる.

He keeps saying the same thing.

かっこいいだろ. うちのボートだぞ.
きみたちをのせてんだぞ.

Isn't this boat cool? It's ours. You're taking our boat.

BRATATATAT

あちい.

IT'S HOT!

ああ, あんまりゆかいで,
のどがかわいた.

Ah, I'm so excited that I'm getting thirsty.

Let's have some hot tea.

あついお茶でものもう.

"Hūko" the typhoon

台風のフー子

チュッ,
チュッ. チュルルル….

Chirp,
chirp...

Peck,
peck.

よくなれてるね. さっ, もうおうちへ
はいりましょうね.

He's so
tame.

Now, it's time
to go back in your
house.

どんな生きものでも, 心から
かわいがれば, きっとなつくわよ. たまごから,
そだてたのよ.

Any animal will be
tame if you care for it
from the heart.

I've raised him
since he was
hatched.

すぐまねを
したがる. ぼくも, 何かたまごから
そだてて, 心から
かわいがりたいな.

You're
such a
copycat.

I want to raise an
animal from a
hatchling,
and care for
it from the
heart
too.

かしてくれよ, そだてるから.

何でも いいじゃない.

なんのたまご だったっけ.

Give it to me. I'll raise it.

Any egg will do.

I can't remember what kind of egg this is.

ええと….

Let me see...

わかった, わかった.

いじめたりすてたり しちゃ, だめだぞ.

OK. OK.

Don't tease it, or abandon it.

何がかえっても, かわいがるんだよ.

いっとくけどね.

No matter what hatches, you have to take care of it.

Just remember.

え, たまごをあたためてるの.

What! You're hatching an egg?

気分でもわるいの.

Do you feel sick?

のび太のためにも, なることだよ.

何でも, かわいがる ことはいいことだ.

This will be good for Nobita.

It's good to care for something, no matter what it is.

まあ, いいじゃ ないか.

ママは, 生きものをかうのは はんたいですからね.

Don't say that.

I'm against keeping animals.

CRACK   Waaaaah   CRACK CRACK

なんだ、これは……。

W, what's this......?

フギャー

パ

ピシッ

ピ
ピ

おおよしよし、いい子だね。

そのたまご、かえしちゃだめだぞっ。

思い出した。

There, there. What a good girl!

Don't let that egg hatch!

I just remembered!

Hoon, hoon.

フーン　フーン。

いや、ほんとはちがうけどさ。

台風って、たまごから生まれるの。

え、台風のたまご。

なんだかしらないけど、かわいいね。ぼくにあまえるんだよ。

No, not usually.

Does a typhoon hatch from an egg?

What! A typhoon egg?

I don't know why, but she's cute. She snuggles with me.

かわいがって、そだててやるんだ。

いやだ、せっかく生まれたのに。

あぶないからすてよう。

気象台の学者が、実験のために作ったものなんだ。

I'll take good care of her.

No. She's already hatched, so...

フーン　フーン。

Hoon, hoon.

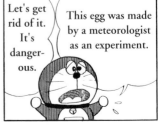

Let's get rid of it. It's dangerous.

This egg was made by a meteorologist as an experiment.

おまえ，ねぞうが
わるいぞ！

あまえんぼ！

えっ，ふとんに
いれてくれって？

You're too restless!

OK, honey!

What? You want to sleep in my *futon*?

フーン フーン

HMMMMMN

Hoon, hoon.

あ，こら，
ふざけちゃだめ.

キャッ！

かわいいわね.

どこへでもついてきたがって
こまるんだ. しっ, しっ.

Hey, stop fooling around.

Yipe!

She's cute.

No matter where I go, she wants to follow me. Shoo, shoo.

だんだん，
いたずらがひどくなる.

フー子が
やったの.

She keeps getting wilder.

Did Hūko do this?

Get rid of her!

あんなの，すててきなさい.

109

Hooo, hooo.

空のさんぽに，
つれてってやる．

Let's go for a walk in the sky.

むちゅうで遊んでる
すきに……．

Now that she's absorbed in playing......

これからおとなしくさせるから，
おしいれにとじこめておくから．

I'll make sure she behaves. I'll keep her up the closet.

フーン，
フーン．

ついてきちゃだめ
だってのに．

Don't follow me!

Hoon, hoon.

こりゃあ，たいへんな
ことになるぞ．

まっすぐこっちへ
くるよう．

This will cause some trouble.

It's coming straight this way.

ものすごい大がた台風が，
日本にむかっています．

An extraordinarily large typhoon is approaching Japan.

110

やねをはがされちゃう.
it'll blow the roof off.

このまま台風が きたら,
If the typhoon comes,

やねのいたんだとこを, まだなおしてなかったわ.
We haven't fixed the damaged roof yet.

THUD

風が強く なってきた.
The wind is getting stronger.

てい電よ.
It's a blackout!

あ, フー子.
Oh, Hūko.

HWOOO　**HOWL**

HOWL

日本からとびだした 小がた台風が,
A small typhoon, coming from Japan,

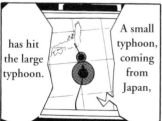

大がた台風に ぶつかりました.
has hit the large typhoon.

どこへいくんだ.
Where are you going?

がんばれ.
Don't give up!

フー子, まけるな.
Hūko, hang in there!

フー子が たたかって いるんだ.
Hūko is fighting.

じつにめずらしいできごとです. 二つの 台風は, からみあったまま動きません.
This is unusual. The two typhoons have intertwined and aren't moving.

台風は，ふたつとも
きえました．

Both
typhoons
have
disappeared.

おっ，風がおさまってきたぞ！

Hey, the wind
is stopping!

フー子……．

Hūko......

小さな風がまっていると，
つい思い出しちゃうんだ．

フー子のことを．

Hūko.

Now whenever
I see a whirlwind,
I remember...

クル

クル

"Kobito Robot"

小人ロボット

よくそんなに
ねられるわね.

How can
you sleep
so much?

のびちゃん, また
おひるねしてるの.

Nobi-chan,
are you taking
a nap again?

こう目をとじて,
1, 2, 3と…….

I close my
eyes like this,
and one, two,
three......

ねようと思えば, いつでも
どこでもねむれるよ.

If I want to sleep,
I can sleep anytime,
anywhere.

ひるねだけは
とくいなんだ.

Taking naps is
the only thing
I'm good at.

やります.　しゅくだいあるんでしょ.

OK.

You have home-
work, don't you?

のびちゃん.　　グウ.

Nobi-chan!

Zzz.

だれのこと.

あのくつやさんは
いいなあ.

Who?

I envy that
shoemaker.

ぼかんと,
なにを考えてるの.

What are you
daydreaming
about?

くつやさんがびょうきになって，しごとをやりかけのまま
ねちゃうんだよ．

The shoemaker got sick, so he went to sleep with his job unfinished.

ほら，どうわに
でてくるじゃない．

You know, the one in that fairy tale.

あるよ．

ねてるまにしごとしてくれる
きかいってないものかなあ．

I wish I could have a machine that would work for me while sleeping.

I have one.

よなかになって，小人たちがあらわれて，
くつをつくってくれたんだ．

At midnight, elves appeared, and made shoes for him.

しゅくだい
たのもう．

これにたのんでねると，
小がたロボットがでてきて
やってくれる．

I'll ask them to do my home-work.

If you ask for something and fall asleep, small robots will appear and work for you.

「小人ばこ」

"Kobito Bako."

ほかのことで
ためしてみよう．

I'll test them to see if they can handle other jobs.

きょうのしゅくだいは
むずかしいんだ．
できるさ．ロボットにできるかな．

They can.

Today's homework is difficult. Can they do it?

まてよ……．

Wait......

ちゃんとやるよ.

I'll do it perfect- ly.

のびちゃんにたのむと, なにやってもしっぱい するんだから.

No matter what job I leave to you, you always mess it up.

いいえ, けっこうよ.

No, thanks.

なにかしごとない？

Do you need any help?

グウ.　　1，2，3…….

Zzz.

One, two, three......

ねなくちゃ いけないのか.

Now I have to fall asleep.

くつみがきをたのまれた. よろしく.

She asked me to polish the shoes. I'll leave it to you.

SCRUB-A-DUB　　**SQUEAK SQUEAK**　　**POP**

ゴシゴシ

キュッキュ

パカ

どんなしごとでも, できるんだ.

They can do any job.

どんな もんです.

Pretty good, eh?

買ったばかり みたいだわ.

They're just like brand- new shoes.

まあ，きれい.

How beautiful!

草むしりが
たいへんなの.

I'm so busy
weeding.

しずちゃん, なにかしごとない.

Shizu-chan, do you
need any help?

1, 2, 3…….
グウ.

One, two,
three......
Zzz.

ひきうけたからあっちへいって.

We'll take care of it,
so go over there.

まあっ, もうおわったの.

Wow, are you
finished already?

くるまのこしょうだ. なおそう.

It looks like
something is wrong
with their car.
Let's fix it.

そんなのねながら　のび太に
なおせらい.　　　なおせるもんか.

I could fix it in my sleep.

There's no way you can fix it.

RUSTLE RUSTLE

すげえ.

Wow.

きみは天さいだ.

You're a genius.

いくらでもひきうけるよ.
じゅんばんにねむって……
いや, かたづけていこう.

I'll take on any job. I'll sleep...... I mean, I'll work for each of you.

おれも.

ぼくも
たのみがある.

うちのせんたくき
なおしてくれよ

Me, too.

I have a favor to ask of you.

Fix our washing machine.

おそかったわね.

You're so late.

やっとおわった.

We're finally finished.

118

Flying fish

空とぶさかな

あっ.

Oh!

きみたちも
かってみな.

Why don't
you raise fish
too?

さかなもなれると,
かわいいよ.

ほくがくんれん
したんだ.

Fish can be
lovable if
they're
tame.

I trained
them.

このへんで，にわに池があるのは,
うちだけだった.

In this neighborhood,
only we have a pond in
the garden.

ごめんごめん.
わるいこといって.

I'm sorry.
I've hurt your
feeling.

よし，うちでも，さかなを
くんれんしよう.

Fine.
We'll train fish,
too.

なにいっ，またスネ夫に
ばかにされたって.

What! Suneo made
fun of you again?

金魚ばちもないのに.

We don't
even have
a gold-
fish
bowl.

We
can't do
that.

むりいうな.

122

金魚なんか，つんまないよ．

では さっそく．

I'm not interested in goldfish.

OK, now...

たのもしいなあ．

何もなくても いいんだ．

Such confidence.

We don't need anything.

They're free.

Aren't they expensive?

ただだよ．

高いんだろ．

あまり人のかってない さかながいいよ．

We want the kind of fish not many people have.

Take a handful.

ひとつかみとって．

げっ，海の中からとるの．

Urk, are we going to catch them in the sea?

123

Now sprinkle it over the sea.

においを
つけて.

ぎゅっと,
にぎって.

Get your body scent on it.

Squeeze it tightly.

SQUEEZE

SPLASH

**SPLASH
SPLASH**

このえさを食べると,
空気の中でも生きていられるんだ.

きゃっ, さかながとんでくる.

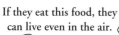

If they eat this food, they can live even in the air.

And they'll be tame with whoever gave them the food.

Ah! There are fish coming toward us.

そして, えさを
くれた人に, なれるんだよ.

124

ほらね，しっぽをふって，
ついてくるよ．

See? They're following us wagging their tails.

池もないくせに．　　　えっ，さかなを
　　　　　　　　　　かってる．

You don't even have a pond in your garden!

What? You're raising fish?

TWEET

It must be tadpoles or something.

おたまじゃくしか
なんかだろう．

FLAP FLAP

さん歩させよう.

Let's take them for a walk.

くやしい. うらやましい.

I can't stand it. I'm so jealous.

すごい. 道くさくっちゃだめだよ.

That's great. Don't dawdle.

ひとつかみとってやれ.

I'll just grab a handful.

CONK **CONK** **SPURT**

127

ぼくのおじさんは
船長だ.

でも, ひとつかみ
とったぞ.

るすばんが,
いたのか.

My uncle is a ship's captain.

He always goes abroad by ship.

At least I grabbed a handful of it.

So there were guard fish.

いつも船で,
外国へ行くんだった.

どんなさかながくるか
楽しみだ. ウシシ.

そう, なるべく
海のまん中で.

これを
ばらまけって.

I can't wait to see what kind of fish come. Heh heh heh.

Yes, right in the middle of the sea, if possible.

You want me to scatter this over the sea?

うわあ, へんなさかながついてきちゃったよ.

Ahh! Some strange fish have showed up.

Eek! Help!

きゃあっ, たすけてざます.

See? They're
following us wagging
their tails.

DORAEMON
Gadget Cat from the Future

BOWWOW
MEOW

けんかしちゃだめよ.

Stop fighting.

どうしてそんなになかがわるいの.

How come you can't get along?

MEEOW

It's because there are two of them. You should put them together into one.

2ひきいるからさ.1ぴきにまとめればいいんだよ.

Put the dog and the cat at either end......

This is the "Ultra Mixer".

りょうはしに,犬とねこをつけて…….

「ウルトラミキサー」だよ.

130

"Ultra Mixer"

ウルトラミキサー

BOW
MEOW

ワニャン

Oh, they disapp-eared.

あっ、きえた.

VOOOM
CLICK

VOOOM CLICK いい考えだ.

132

くずかごと
まとめたよ.

だれかそうじ機を
知らない.

We put it together with the waste-basket.

Does anybody know where the vacuum cleaner is?

テレビをどこへ
やったんだ.

いちいち, すてなくていい
から, たすかるでしょ.

VVVVV

Where's the TV?

You don't have to take the trouble to throw the dust away. Isn't that helpful?

ス!

へんな気もち.

タンスとまとめたよ.

This feels weird.

It was put together with chest of drawers.

トースターと
まとめたのさ.

POP

なんだかへんな形に
なっているわ.

アイロンが,

We put it together with the toaster.

ポン

changed into a strange shape.

The iron has been

133

カミソリと, ライターを
くっつけました.

あちいっ. **FLICK**

Vrrrr

We put the razor and the lighter together.

Ouch.

トイレと
いっしょ.

どこへやっ
たのよっ. れいぞうこを,

We put it together with the toilet.

Where is it?

The refrigerator!

いい考えだと
思ったのに.

すぐもとに
もどして！

いいかげんに
しなさい.

We thought they were such good ideas.

Put everything back to normal at once!

That's enough!

おやつは,
ふたりで一つよ.

おしいなあ.

ほかにつかいみち
ないかなあ.

There's only one cake for the two of you.

It's too bad.

Isn't there something else we could use it for?

134

そうだ. あのミキサーで,

Hey. We can use that mixer.

ぼくだって.

Neither do I.

半分なんていやだ.

I don't want just half.

なんにも分けなくていいね.

we don't have to share anything.

これからもずっとひとりでいれば,

If we are one from now on,

のびえもんだよ.

I'm Nobi-emon.

ひとりでけんかしているのはだれですっ.

THUD THUD

昼ね.

あそぶ.

Who fights by himself?

A nap.

Play!

あそびに行こう.

Let's go play.

No, let's take a nap.

いや, 昼ねしようよ.

135　てんとう虫コミックス「ドラえもん」第7巻　収録作品

"Esper Boushi"

エスパーぼうし

胴（どう）を切りはなして
またつなぐ。

I'll cut you in half and put you back together again.

ちょっと
そこへねて。

じゃべつのを
やる。

?

Lie down.

?

OK, I'll try a different one.

WHIZZZZ

あっ，ぼくを
みすてるのか。

Hey, don't give up on me!

テレビでは，
かんたんそうだったよ。

まった！やりかた
しってるんだろうね。

It looked easy on TV.

Wait! Do you know how to do it?

みんなをアッと
いわせるからな。

あったり
まえさあ。

I'll astonish everybody.

Of course.

スネ夫くん，かくしげい
なにをやるかきめた？

Suneo-kun, have you decided what trick to do?

まずいなあ，パーティは
今夜なのに。

What can I do? The party is tonight.

今夜をたのしみにしてな。
アッといわせてやるから。

See you tonight. I'll astonish you.

なにをやるかないしょだけど，
まあ，アッといわせる
自信はあるの。

I won't tell you my parlor trick, but I'm sure I'll astonish everybody.

なにをやるって？
それはひみつだよ。

You want to know my trick? It's a secret.

CLICK

138

139

だめなんだ
それが.

I'm sorry
I can't.

おもしろい！
かしてかして.

Sounds like
fun! Lend it
to me.

遠くはなれていたり，物かげ
などの見えない物を見る.

You can see
things that are
far away or
hidden.

clairvoyance

透視（とうし）＝クレヤボヤンス

かなりれんしゅうしないと
これはつかいこなせない.

It takes a lot of training to
operate   this.

いうもんか.

I
promise.

ようし！じゃ，もうれんしゅうだ.
とちゅうでいやだなんていうなよ.

All right! Then, let's train
hard. You can't give up
halfway
through.

ぼくはあせって
いるんだぞ！

I don't have
much time
left!

はいざらを
うごかしてごらん.

Move
that
ashtray.

かるいものから
いこう.

Let's start with
something
light.

さいしょは
テレキネシス.

First,
try
teleki-
nesis.

もっといっしょう
けんめいおもう.

心の中で，うごけ
うごけとおもう.

ジイッと
みつめて…….

Think
harder.

Think
"Move,
move".

You stare
at it,
and
......

すぐとどけるから. 　いるんだよ.

I'll bring
it to you
soon.

But I
need
it.

ああ. 　　　ああ.

Hey.

Oh.

おうい，まだかい.

Hey, aren't
you finished
yet?

まだまだ，
もっともっと.

いっしょうけんめい，
おもってるのに.

It's not
enough.
Try
hard-
er.

I'm think-
ing as
hard as
I can,
but...

そのちょうしだっ.

That's
the way.

スッ

WHISK

もうひといき！

Just
one
more
go!

カタ
カタ

**CLATTER
CLATTER**

おっ.

Oh.

FIZZLE

142

どいて！！

Get out of the way!

う～～～～～. がんばれ. TOTTER おとすな.

UM-----

Stick to it.

Don't drop it.

Sorry to keep you waiting......, puff, puff.

ゴイン

おまちどお……, ハアハア. BANG!

ようし, ざぶとんはできたね.

OK. You could move the cushion.

ヒイ ハア
ヒイ. ハア.

Huff, huff.

Puff, puff.

UM-- UM--

トイレに いきたいんだよお.

I want to go to the bathroom.

だめっ. そんなひまないぞ.

No. We don't have time for a break.

ちょ, ちょっと ひと休み.

Wait. I need a break.

だんだん重くしよう. つぎはこれ.

Let's try something heavier. Next do this.

143

心の中でトイレに
なげなわをひっかけるんだ.

Imagine you throw a lasso at the toilet.

じゃ, テレポーテーション
でいこう.

Then, let's use teleportation.

そらっ, からだが
ひっぱられてる.

There you go! Your body is being pulled.

それをグイッと
たぐりよせるかんじ.

And haul on it.

Arr!

せいいっぱい
だよっ.

This is the limit.

もっと力を
いれてっ!もっと.

Put more power into it! More!

RATTLE RATTLE

ああああああ.

Oh, no...

BAANG!

Urk.

ゲ.

つぎはクレヤボヤンス.

やるときめたら
とことんやるんだ.

Next, clair-voyance.

Once you decide to do it, you have to do it right.

なにを
いまさら.

It's too late to say that now.

やっぱりむりだよ.
なにかほかのことしよう.

I can't do it. I'll try something different.

そんな
むりな……….

That's impossible...

なるべく遠くの家のかげで
見えないところを見よう.

Try to look at a place far away and behind a house.

もっと
もっと.

More power.

目に力をいれて！

Put power into your eyes!

たいしたこと
ないや.

Nothing special.

ハンカチのでる
手品だな.

The trick pulling hand-kerchiefs out.

あっ，家が
すきとおってみえる！

Hey, I can look right through the house.

こちらは人形とダンスか.
たいしたことない.

Dancing with a doll. Nothing special.

タネまで
みえる.

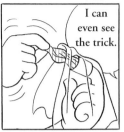

I can even see the trick.

じゃ,
あんしんだね.

ほかのだれのも
パッとしないや.

That's a relief.

Nobody else astonishes me.

へそおどり, くうだらない.

Belly button dance. Nonsense!

げんかんに
だしといたんだ.

なくなった!?

I put it by the door.

It's gone!?

あのほうしさえ
あれば.

ぼくのが
いちばんだ.

As long as I have that cap.

I'm No.1.

BRRRING

いぬでも
くわえていったかな.

じょうだんじゃない.
もうでかける時こくだぞ.

Maybe a dog took it.

What can I do? It's time to go.

146

みつかったら
もってきて.

さきに
いってる.

あと５分いないにこなければ
けっ席とみとめる！

If you
find it,
bring it
to me.

I'll go
to his
house.

If you don't come
within 5 minutes,
we'll assume you're
not
coming.

やって見せろ.
さあ, 見せろ.

ようよう, えらそうなこと
いったな. テレなんとかだって？

Show us.
Come on,
show us.

Hey, hey. You
talk pretty big.
You're going
to do "Tele...
something"?

なんだとおれさまのだぞ.

ばあか, いちばん
おもしろいのはぼくのだい.

いちばんおもしろいのは,
いちばんあとだよ.
しょくんからどうぞ.

No. Mine is!

You fool. My
performance is the
most   interesting.

The most interesting
performance should
be done last.
You go first.

ふしぎな手品だぞ.

This is mysterious magic.

エヘン！アッと おどろくな.

Ahem. You'll all be astonished.

チェッ，1番.

Tsk! I'm the first.

くじ引きで，じゅんばんを きめましょう.

Let's draw straws to decide the order.

あほらしい. やめた.

Forget it. I give up.

はりきって どうぞ.

Go ahead.

パチパチ

CLAP CLAP

テレビで タネあかし やってた.

The trick was revealed on TV.

Oh, I know that trick.

なんだ，そんなら 知ってるわ.

He'll pull out lots of handkerchiefs.

ハンカチがたくさんでるんだ,

まってました， ヘソおどり！

I couldn't wait for your "belly button dance".

おもしろくておもしろくて， ひっくりかえるぞ.

It's so funny that you'll be astonished.

おれのはな，めっちゃ くちゃにおもしろいんだぞ.

Mine is really funny.

いやあねえ. エッチ.

Oh, no. How perverted!

まっ， 下品！

How vulgar!

おなかに顔をかいて おどるんだよ.

He'll write a face on his stomach and dance.

Bye.

さいなら.

そうだ
そうだ.

That's right.

ひとのことばかりいわずに,
じぶんのをみせろ.

Stop talking about our performance. Show us yours.

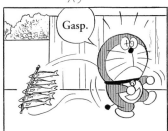

ハッ

Gasp.

「エスパーぼうし」やあい.

Where's that "Esper *Boushi*"?

だれだろう.

Who is it?

さてはだれかが
「エスパーぼうし」を.

Someone must be using it.

It's......

あれは……

みつかったよ.

I found it.

あった.

There it is.

Now I'll get even with them!

みてろ！あのふたり.

テレキネシス!!

WHISK

Teleki-nesis!!

それもかくしげいなの？

Is that your parlor trick, too?

WHOOP WHOOP

あんなこと　いってる！

You hear what they're saying?

すごうい.

そうなんだ.

That's great!

That's right.

Y, yeah! Actually, this is our parlor trick.

CLAP CLAP

そ, そう！じつはこれが　ぼくらのかくしげい.

服だけいっちゃった．

ようし．

テレポーテーション
でとびこめ．

POOOOF!

てんとう虫コミックス「ドラえもん」
第7巻　収録作品

そら，もうすこしだ！！

英語力を高める ワン・ポイント レッスン

このコミックでは、意味がわかりやすく、そしてふだんよく使われる英語表現を選んで使用しています。ここでは、さらに英語の理解を深めるために、いくつかの英語表現について例をあげてご説明します。

9ページ4段目

いいね. あとで…….

Sound good. Later ……

きみは、「クイック」を飲みなさい.

Take some "QUICK".

このsoundは「音」という意味の名詞ではなく、「…と聞こえる、…のようだ」という意味の動詞です。口語ではよく主語が省略されて、Sound [Sounds] good.（いいね）のように用います。

10ページ1段目

じゃ, まず自分で飲んでみせろ！

Fine, but you try it first!

fineはもともと「すぐれた、りっぱな、よい」という意味ですが、場合によっては、「それはそれでオーケーだ」くらいの軽いニュアンスになります。19、48ページにも、同じような使い方があります。

11ページ4段目

Rat-tat-tat

じれったいな, もう.

I can't take it any-more.

このtake itは、口語表現で「たえる、(いやなことを)受け入れる」の意味です。ふつうcanやcannotといっしょに用いて、「たえられる」「たえられない」を表します。

12ページ4段目

やきいもは, 食べるまえにおならをする.

Pass gas before you eat baked sweet potatoes.

BOM

passはいろいろな意味をもつ動詞ですが、ここでは「排泄(はいせつ)する」を表しています。pass waterなら、「小便をする」という意味です。

16ページ2段目

ねえ. 消えるでしょ.

its effect.

Right?

ききめが, いつか, 薬なら,

lose eventually The medicine will

「ききめが」の英訳がlose(消える)、「消えるでしょ」の英訳がits effect(ききめ)となっていますが、ひとつの文の中で日本語と英語の語順が違うためにこのようにしてあります。18ページの1段1こま目も同様です。

46ページ1段目

男なら投げかえせ！
そんなめにあわされて、だまって帰ってきたのか！

Be a man! Throw him down!

And you just came home with your tail between your legs?

with one's tail between one's legsは、犬が自分のしっぽをうしろ足の間にはさんだすがたから、「しょげた、おじけづいた」ようすを表しています。日本語にも、「しっぽをまいて」という同じような表現がありますね。

47ページ1段目

そうとも！
これで、ジャイアンのやつにしかえしができる.

That's right!

Using this, I can get even with Gian.

「…にしかえしをする」という意味のget even with …を使っています。「…」には、しかえしをする相手が入ります。be even with …も、同じ意味です。

78ページ1段目

この気の弱いの、なんとかなおせないかなあ.

I want to get rid of this cowardliness somehow.

「好ましくないもの、いやなもの」を「取りのぞく」ときに、get rid of …を用います。
I cannot get rid of this cold.（かぜがぬけない）のようにも使えます。

90ページ3段目

これ
どういうこと？

What's
going on?

よくおわびしなさい！

Be sure to
apologize to
her.

さあ、はいりなさい．
スネ太郎くんのママが
かんかんよ．

Now, get
inside.
Sunetaro's
mom is
blowing her
top.

blow one's topは「かんかんに怒る」を意味する、かなりくだけた表現です。このtopは「ふた、栓（せん）」をさしていますが、頭のふたを吹き飛ばすほど怒っているようすを思い浮かべてみてください。

91ページ2段目

ママにむかって
きみとはなんです．

What do you
mean saying
"YOU" like that
to your mother?

日本語では自分の親にむかって「きみ」というのはよくありませんが、英語ではSo, it's you, is it?と、youを使ってまったく問題はありません。ここではのび太の口ぶりがくだけすぎたとかいしゃくして、次のママのセリフ中のYOUを強調しています。

101ページ2段目

もうすぐ海だ．

We'll get
to the beach
soon.

へんなとこ
ばっかり．

We keep
ending up
in weird
places.

end up …は「終わりには…になる」を表しますが、この場合ジャンプした結果到着した場所が「…」に入っています。keep doingは「…し続ける」ですから、ジャンプするたびに変な場所に着いてしまっていることになります。

105ページ4段目

すぐまねを
したがる.

You're
such a
copycat.

ほくも, 何かたまごから
そだてて, 心から
かわいがりたいな.

I want to raise an
animal from a
hatchling,
and care for
it from the
heart
too.

copycatは口語で「人まねをする人」の意味ですが、やや軽べつ的なニュアンスをふくんでいて「まねっこ」ぐらいの感じになります。動物を表す語が人をさすものには、top dog「勝者、重要人物」などもあります。

126ページ4段目

このえさを,
ギュッとにぎってだね

I just squeezed
this food tightly,
and...

いい, いったい
どうやって.

How on earth
did you do it?

このon earthは、疑問詞といっしょに用いて「いったい全体」と強調する働きをします。What on earth …?なら「いったい何が…」、Who on earth …?なら「いったいだれが…」となります。肯定文(こうていぶん)で使われる場合は、「地上で、この世で」という意味になります。

147ページ3段目

ば, ばかにすんな.

Don't
make light
of me!

「…を軽視(けいし)する、…を軽んじる」を表すmake light of …を使っています。反対に「…を重視する」というなら、make much of …となります。

Doraemon②

SHOGAKUKAN ENGLISH COMICS

アートディレクション／海野一雄
カバーデザイン／鈴木麻里子＋ベイブリッジ・スタジオ
カバーイラスト／むぎわらしんたろう ©藤子プロ
英訳・編集協力／(株)ジャレックス
DTP協力／(有)オフィス・エヌ (株)プロセスセンター
英訳協力／VIZ COMMUNICATIONS INC.
協力／(株)小学館プロダクション
単行本編集責任／山川史郎

2002年 6 月20日　　初版第 1 刷発行	（検印廃止）
2007年10月27日　　　第13刷発行	

著　者　　　藤 子・F・不 二 雄
　　　　　　©藤 子 プ ロ　　2002

発行者　　　宮　木　立　雄

印刷所　　　文 唱 堂 印 刷 株 式 会 社
製本所　　　株式会社 難 波 製 本　　　PRINTED IN JAPAN

発行所　（〒101-8001）東京都千代田区一ツ橋二の三の一　株式会社 小学館
　　　　　　TEL 販売03(5281)3555 編集03(3230)5685

ISBN4-09-227012-7

SHOGAKUKAN ENGLISH COMICS